10 9 8 7 6 5 4 3 2 1

Published by Sterling Publishing Company, Inc.
387 Park Avenue South, New York, N.Y. 10016

Material in this collection was adapted from
The Craziest Riddle Book in the World © Lori Miller Fox
Oodles of Riddles © Lori Miller Fox
Wild West Riddles and Jokes © Joseph Rosenbloom

Distributed in Canada by Sterling Publishing
c/o Canadian Manda Group, One Atlantic Avenue, Suite 105
Toronto, Ontario, Canada M6K 3E7

Distributed in Great Britain and Europe by Chris Lloyd
463 Ashley Road, Parkstone, Poole, Dorset, BH14 0AX,
United Kingdom

Distributed in Australia by Capricorn Link (Australia) Pty Ltd
P.O. Box 6651, Baulkham, Business Centre, NSW 2153, Australia

Sterling ISBN 0-8069-7108-8

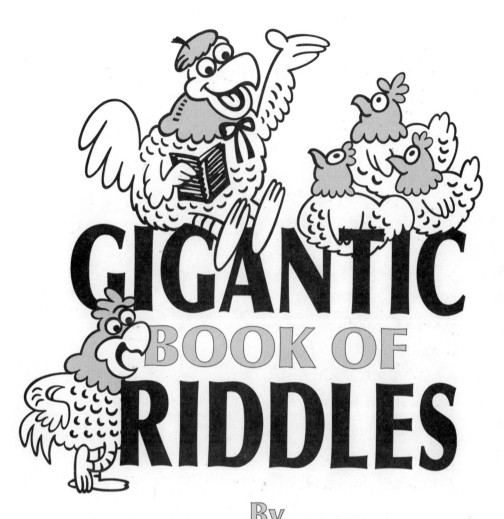

GIGANTIC
BOOK OF
RIDDLES

By
LORI MILLER FOX
JOSEPH ROSENBLOOM

Illustrations By
SANFORD HOFFMAN

The Main Street Press

Contents

1
Wacky Warm-ups

What do jigsaw puzzles do when they get bad news?
Go to pieces.

What ice cream do monkeys eat?
Chocolate chimp.

What do archaeologists dig up at baboon burial grounds?
Ba-bones.

Who helped the werewolf go to the ball?
Its Hairy Godmother.

What two-ton animal can put you in a trance?
A hypnopotamus.

What do members of the Scooby Doo fan club pay?
Scooby dues.

Who is Scooby Doo's evil twin?
Scooby Don't.

Where do fish go to get a degree?
To tuna-versities.

How do loudmouths pay for college?
They get hollerships.

What do mechanics do in aerobics class?
Touch their tow trucks.

Why did the mother horse scold her little colt?
For misbehooving.

How do you hit slime?
With a sludgehammer.

How do baby birds know how to fly?
They just sort of wing it.

What did the parrot say to the streetcar?
"Trolley want a cracker?"

Why did the chicken cross the
amusement park?
To get to the other ride.

What's the difference between a lollipop and a chicken?
One you suck and one you pluck.

How do you measure an aardvark?
With an aardstick.

What star slept for 100 years?
Rip Van Twinkle.

How do frightened skydivers scream for help?
They parashout.

If you buy doughnuts by the dozen, how do you buy bees?
By the buzzin'.

What would you get if you crossed a spider with a duck?
A bug that spins webbed feet.

What do you call an unidentified flying cow?
A Moo-F-O (UFO).

SILLY SUBSCRIPTIONS

What's a frog's favorite magazine?
"Warts (Sports) Illustrated."

What's a lawyer's favorite magazine?
"Courts Illustrated."

What's a clothing manufacturer's favorite magazine?
"Shorts Illustrated."

Where do customers trade merchandise?
In swapping malls (shopping malls).

Who delivers trees overnight?
Federal Exspruce.

Where do dead letters go?
To the Ghost Office.

What would you get if you crossed an alligator with a pickle?
A crocodill.

How do ugly ducklings live their lives?
Swan (one) day at a time.

What long-necked bird can't be seen?
Casper the Friendly Goose (Ghost).

What's the difference between a stool pigeon in jail and a monkey in the zoo?
One sings behind bars, the other swings behind bars.

What's Santa's ethnic background?
North Polish.

Why was Santa's Little Helper depressed?
He has low elf-esteem.

How does Santa communicate in Morse code?
With dots and Dashers (dashes).

2
Feature Creatures

Where did animals play video games during the great flood?

In Noah's Arc-ade.

What's the difference between a lizard, a crybaby, and the Roadrunner?

One creeps, one weeps, and one beeps.

Why did the amoeba take two aspirins?
Its head was splitting.

What animals can survive the coldest weather?
Polar brrrrs.

What bear never bathes?
Winnie-the-Phew.

What bears live in Tokyo?
Japan-da bears.

What dog is always smiling?
Grin Tin Tin.

Where does Santa dog paddle?
In the North Pool.

What tricks can you teach a dog in a beauty parlor?
To comb (come), set (sit), and roller over.

What would you get if you crossed a beautician with a dog?
A shampoodle.

What do you lend to a needy vet?
    A helping hound (hand).

Where do smart dogs refuse to shop?
    At flea markets.

Do cats confide in each other?
    Yes, they purr (pour) their hearts out.

What does a vet keep outside his front door?
    A welcome mutt.

What scatterbrained creature climbed up the water spout?
  The itsy ditzy (bitsy) spider.

What insect is hardest to understand?
  A mumble bee.

What do you hear when you dial a talkative bee?
  A buzzy signal.

What do counselors lead at bee camp?
  Sting-alongs (sing-alongs).

What kills flies by sitting on them?
  A fly squatter.

How do you revive a butterfly that has fainted?
With moth-to-moth resuscitation.

What does a crazy butterfly come out of?
A kook-oon.

What has many legs, antennae and a sack of toys over its shoulder?
A Santa-pede (centipede).

What did Scrooge's sheep say to the mosquito at Christmas?
"Baaaa—humbug."

Why did the lamb go out in the middle of the night?
It was sheep walking (sleepwalking).

How did the shepherd's flock look?
Sheepshape.

What nursery rhyme character is half elephant and half lamb?
Babar (Baa Baa) Black Sheep.

What do you get when an elephant sits on squash?
Squish.

What did the mother groundhog say to encourage her baby?
"Gopher (go for) it!"

MEAN, GREEN & IN THEIR TEENS

What Teenage Mutant Ninja Turtle
shakes when he walks?
Michelan-jello.

What do Teenage Mutant Ninja Turtles
call each other on?
The Dona-tellophone.

What Teenage Mutant Ninja Turtle
is grey, wrinkled, and weighs two tons?
Rapha-elephant.

What do Teenage Mutant Ninja Turtles
get milk from?
Cow Bungas.

What animal hangs around caves and wins spelling bees?
  An alpha-bat.

What poisonous snake is most spoiled by its parents?
  A brattlesnake.

What lizard eats lots of lettuce?
  A salad-mander.

Who's the most boring alligator?
  A crocodull.

What snake builds things?
  A boa constructor.

What does Charlie the Tuna get from his admirers?
Fin (fan) mail.

What happens when you try to recognize sea mammals?
You can't tell one from the otter.

What did the decorator put on the ocean floor?
Whale-to-whale (wall-to-wall) carpeting.

What did the big bird say to the little bird?
"You're a chirp (chip) off the old flock (block)."

What would you get if you crossed an owl with Santa Claus?
A bird that says, "Whooo whooo whooo."

DID YOU HEAR?

Did you hear the one about the owl?
Yes, it was a hoot.

Did you hear the one about the wolf?
Yes, it made me howl.

Did you hear the one about the lion?
Yes, it made me roar.

Did you hear the one about the skunk?
Yes, it stank.

What would you get if you crossed an idiot with a baby chick?

A ninny-compeep (nincompoop).

What would you get if you crossed a chicken with a cow?
Roost beef.

What do roosters pay when they join clubs?
Cock-a-doodle dues.

What would you get if you crossed a cow with Bullwinkle?
A moo-se.

What naughty cow jumps off buildings for fun?
A dairy (dare) devil.

What do you say when choosing a cow?
"Eenie, meenie, miney, moo . . ."

What's the phone company's favorite Christmas song?
"Jingle Bulls."

What did the doctor order when the bull broke its leg?
An ox-ray.

What would you get if you crossed patriotic American oxen with patriotic American zebras?
Steers (stars) and stripes.

How did the Three Little Pigs know the Big Bad Wolf was mad?
He left in a huff.

What sizes do skunks come in?
Large, medium and smell.

Why did the little skunk listen to the big skunk?
Because it was odor (older) and wiser.

What did Bambi put on the back of his car?
A Thumper sticker.

What do you call a furry black animal with a white stripe and purple hair?
A skunk rocker.

What would you get if you crossed a hippopotamus with a rodent?

A hippopota-mouse.

What would you get if you crossed a hippopotamus with a rabbit?

A hop-popotamus.

Was that a rabbit I saw?
No. It was a hoptical illusion.

What would you get if you crossed a rabbit with computer software?

A bunny with floppy ears.

3
What's Cooking?

What happens when you add detergent to chicken noodle soup?

It becomes chicken noodle soap.

Where do you buy food for dinner?

In a suppermarket.

What's the difference between a diet and a crowded elevator?

One is hard to go on and one is hard to get off.

What's the difference between Peter Pan and a child who doesn't want to eat soap?

One doesn't want to grow up, the other doesn't want to throw up.

What do little chefs do for homework?

Cook-book reports.

How do lions like their meat cooked?
Medium roar.

How do straight-A students like their meat cooked?

Well done.

What's the most popular fast food in Italy?

Big Mac-aroni.

What fast food can't stop talking?

A Big Yak (Big Mac).

What does a frog order at a fast food restaurant?

A burger and flies.

What's Pinocchio's favorite dessert?

Chocolate liar (layer) cake.

What is a frog asked when it comes into a restaurant?
Croaking or non-croaking (non-smoking)?

Who eats chow mein every single day?
A chow mein-iac (maniac).

What does a little dog spread cream cheese on?
A puppyseed beagle (poppyseed bagel).

Why did the baker insult the bread?
To get a rise out of it.

Why do waiters make good soldiers?
They're used to taking orders.

DID YOU HEAR?

Did you hear the one about the tomato?
Yes, it was rotten.

Did you hear the one about the cracker?
Yes, it was crumby.

Did you hear the one about the onion?
Yes, I laughed so hard I cried.

Did you hear the one about the broken egg?
Yes, it cracked me up.

What vegetables always get extra special attention?
V.I.Peas (V.I.P.s).

What do you say when choosing vegetables?
"Zucchini, meenie, miney, moe . . ."

What does a lima bean wear on its head?
A lima beanie.

What is the difference between a baby and a cucumber?
One is tickled, the other is pickled.

What fairy tale tells the story of an unattractive wonton that becomes beautiful?
The Ugly Dumpling.

What do traitors order for breakfast?
Eggs Benedict Arnold.

What do you get if you pour maple syrup on Mickey Mouse?

Sticky Mouse.

Who does Tinkerbell pour syrup on?

Peter Pancake.

If you make hamburgers from ground beef, what do you make pork burgers from?

Groundhogs.

What do you say when choosing a hot dog?

"Weenie, meenie, miney, moe . . ."

What would you get if you crossed a chicken with a porcupine?

I don't know, but if you cook it in boiling water, you get chicken needle soup.

What's the difference between an ice-cream cone and a spoiled brat?

One gets a licking for being good, and the other gets a licking for being bad.

What decaffeinated coffee did they serve on the Titanic?

Sank-a.

Where are mashed potatoes buried?

In gravy yards.

What do successful people feed their dogs?
    Yuppie Chow.

What happens to a boysenberry pie when you put arsenic in it?
    It becomes a poisonberry pie.

What do salad makers do while they sleep?
    Toss and turn.

What dressing does Robinson Crusoe put on his salad?
    Thousand Island.

How do librarians file melted marshmallows?
    According to the Gooey (Dewey) Decimal System.

What would you get if you crossed a tomato, some cheese, and a mail carrier?

A pizza that delivers itself.

Where do tiny macaroni and itty bitty meatballs come from?

L'Italy (Little-y).

What dish is served in Italy on New Year's Eve?

Confetti and meatballs.

What has cheese and pepperoni and is psychic?

E.S.Pizza.

4
Crazy Careers

What does a snake charmer wear around his neck?
A boa (bow) tie.

What kind of shoes do gas station attendants wear with dresses?
Pumps.

Why are locksmiths such good singers?
They're always on key.

What's the difference between a hotel clerk and a detective?

> *One checks people in and one checks people out.*

What's the difference between a pilot and a carpenter?

> *One boards planes, the other planes boards.*

What's the difference between a deep thinker and an explorer?

> *One wonders, the other wanders.*

What does Sherlock Holmes read for fun?

> *The ency-clue-pedia.*

What do police learn in school?

> *How to tell crime (time).*

If baby sitters get paid by the hour, how do florists get paid?
By the flower.

What does Robocop wear to keep the sun off his head?
Robocap.

What does Robocop drink milk from?
Robocup.

Who can make popcorn and compose music at the same time?
Orville Redden-bach.

Do composers write long letters?
No, they write short notes.

How does a Yankee draw?
A Yankee doodles dandy.

Who was the most spoiled artist?
Rem-brat (Rembrandt).

On what faraway planet don't they recycle their garbage?
Polluto (Pluto).

What do you call thieves who steal only windshield wipers?
Windshield swipers.

What are a banker's favorite vowels?
I-O-U.

DID YOU HEAR?

Did you hear the one about Napoleon?
Yes, it was historical (hysterical).

Did you hear the one about the angry mob?
Yes, it was a riot.

Did you hear the one about the tailor?
Yes, it had me in stitches.

Did you hear the one about the stupid kid?
Yes, but I didn't get it.

Did you hear the one about the amnesia patient?
Yes, but I forgot how it went.

Did you hear the one about the caveman?
Yes, ages ago.

How do Bullwinkle and his wife sign in at a hotel?
As Mister and Mooses (Mrs.).

If Vanna White and Pat Sajak got married, what would they exchange at the ceremony?
Wedding vow-els.

How did the hangman get married?
He tied the knot.

Who married the Jolly Green Giant and his wife?
A Justice of the Peas (Peace).

What is the biblical story of an underachiever named Bart and a woman who cut hair?
  Simpson and Delilah.

Who were the most trusting biblical characters?
  Adam and Naive (Eve).

What did Adam and Eve name their two dogs?
  Canine (Cain) and Abel.

What lion was queen of Egypt?
  Leo-patra.

Why did the two-timing
groomcross the road?
To get to the other bride.

What did Santa's little elves do in aerobics class?
Touch their mistle-toes.

Why did the sheik ask his wives to repeat what they said?
Because he couldn't harem (hear 'em).

Why did the photographer throw a grenade into the dark-
room?
To blow up his pictures.

Why are cameramen hard to get along with?
They have too many videosyncrasies (idiosyncrasies).

Why did the maid stop pressing shirts?
She decided to go on strike while the iron was hot.

What does a tailor use to repair a flat tire?
A needle and tread (thread).

Who is the nastiest Disney character?
Meanie Mouse.

If Native Americans used to meet at powwows, where did their dogs meet?
At bowwows.

Where did farmers and Native Americans meet?
At plow-wows.

What was Old MacDonald's nickname when he was in the army?
G-I-G-I-Joe (E-I-E-I-O).

What herring ruled Russia?
The czar-dine (sardine).

SHRINKS HIGH JINKS?

Why did the astronaut go to the psychiatrist?
Because he was space-y.

Why did the body of water go to the psychiatrist?
For psycho-canal-ysis (psychoanalysis).

Why did the broken leg go to the psychiatrist?
It had a splint personality.

Why did the Dairy Queen go to the psychiatrist?
She had a banana split personality.

Why did the car go to the psychiatrist?
It had a brake-down.

What does a yes man do when he's tired?
He nods off.

Is he the real spaghetti-maker?
No, he's an impasta (imposter).

If dentists pull police officers' teeth out, what do police officers do to dentists' teeth?
Pull them over.

What would you get if you crossed a dentist with a military officer?
A drill sergeant.

Who would you get if you crossed a nearsighted cartoon character with a baby?
Mr. Magoo-goo.

What would you get if you crossed Betty Crocker with Old Man Winter?
A baker who frosts windows.

What did one coal worker say to the other coal worker?
"Mine your own business."

What do astronauts carry on their ships in the winter?
Space heaters.

What do authors have when they're too nervous to write?
Page (stage) fright.

Who can write a children's book and give a great massage at the same time?
Dr. Masseuse (Seuss).

What did little Tarzan's mother read to him to help him fall asleep?
Safari (fairy) tales.

Who is the most talkative fairy tale character?
Rap Van Winkle.

What would you get if you crossed a surgeon with a judge?
A judge who can get people hitched and stitched at the same time.

When is a football player like a judge?
When he's on the bench.

How are judges like tennis players?
Both work the courts.

What would you get if you crossed a cartoonist with Benedict Arnold?
An illus-traitor.

What does a vegetarian's car run on?
Aspara-gas.

What's the difference between a practical joker and a reluctant friend?
One is always putting you on, the other is always putting you off.

If kids get a "thank you" from their parents when they do something right, what do they get when they do someting wrong?
A "spank you."

5

A Mad Mad World

What kind of cologne did prehistoric man wear?
After cave (shave).

How did Noah get the marching band onto the ark?
Tuba-two (two-by-two).

How did Noah get trains onto the ark?
Toot-by-toot.

Where did the ancient Egyptians bury magicians?
   In disa-pyramids (disappear-amids).

What do you say when choosing magicians?
   "Houdini, meenie, miney, moe . . ."

What did the sampler in Julius Caesar's house say?
   "Rome Sweet Rome."

Where does Robin Hood buy flowers for Maid Marian?
   At the Sherwood Florist (Forest).

IS THERE A DOCTOR IN THE HOUSE?

What does a sheep say
when it sticks its tongue
out for the doctor?
"Baaah."

What doctor invented the light bulb?
Thomas Medicine (Edison).

What do doctors say on Halloween?
"Trick or Treatment!"

Which one of Adam and Eve's sons was a dentist?
Novo-cain.

What famous painting shows a very sick woman,
coughing, sneezing and smiling?
Pneumonia Lisa (Mona Lisa).

Who handles health club emergencies?
A S.W.E.A.T. (S.W.A.T.) team.

What is a surgeon's favorite musical?
Phantom of the Opera-tion.

DID YOU HEAR?

Did you hear the one about the tornado?
Yes, it blew me away.

Did you hear the one about the carpet?
Yes, it had me on the floor.

Did you hear the one about the airplane?
Yes, but it went over my head.

Did you hear the one about the corn plant?
Yes, it's the stalk (talk) of the town.

What knight rode the fastest horse?
Spur (Sir) Lancelot.

When did knights butt into each other's business?
In the Meddle Ages.

If the children of knights play board games, what do their fathers play?
Sword games.

What ape helped settle the American frontier?
    Daniel Ba-Boone.

What cowboy never said a word?
    Quiet (Wyatt) Earp.

Who was the smallest cowboy?
    Wyatt Twirp.

Who was the funniest gunfighter?
    Groucho Marksman (Marx-man).

What great Italian explorer had four legs and a tail?
Barko (Marco) Polo.

Why did the captain bring the submarine in for repair?
To replace the shark plugs (spark plugs).

Why didn't the sailor tell the submarine the good news?
So it wouldn't get its scopes (hopes) up.

If astronomers measure far distances in light years, how do
birds measure far distances?
In flight years.

What does a sidewalk become when it's icy?
    A slidewalk.

What's slime's motto?
    Goo for it.

What do you say when you tickle slime?
    "Coochy, coochy goo."

What do you say when you tickle a clock?
    "Coochy, coochy cuckoo."

Why are clocks made better and better as time goes by?
    Tick-nology (technology) improves.

What happens when you irritate a clock?
    It gets ticked off.

What do you put on the floor of a baby's room?
    Crawl-to-crawl carpeting.

Who cleans up after Robin Hood and his merry men?
    Maid Marian.

When does a maid work?
    From dawn to dust (dusk).

What's the difference between a star, a suit, and a hose?
    One twinkles, one wrinkles, and one sprinkles.

What would you get if you crossed an X, an O, and a dog from Oz?

Tick-Tack-Toto.

What did the Kleenex write on the postcard?

"Tissue (wish you) were here."

What's the difference between a host and a tycoon?

One takes company in and one takes companies over.

What would you get if you mixed your mother's red nail polish with her orange nail polish?

In trouble.

If you pay for fruit by the pound, how do you pay for dirt?

By the mound.

What store has the most agreeable salespeople?

O.K.-Mart.

What do Native American plumbers install?

Peace pipes.

Who is the smallest dictator?

A ty-runt.

What do dictators wipe their feet on?

Diplo-mats.

In what part of California do wealthy woodchucks live?
Beaverly Hills.

Do rubber bands lie?
No, they just stretch the truth.

Who hid on Jacques Cousteau's ship?
A Cousteau-away (stowaway).

If fish travel in schools, how does thread travel?
In spools.

When do Eskimos travel in heavy traffic?
At mush (rush) hour.

What U.S. president got hit by a truck?
George Squashington.

What mouse heads the House of Representatives?
The Squeaker of the House.

Why did the movie star build an ark?
In case he got flooded with fan mail.

What state has the most streets?
Road (Rhode) Island.

How far is it from one town to the next on an unpaved road?
Just a hop, skip and a bump.

What's harder than catching a train when you're late?
Throwing one.

What did the riverbed say when it agreed with the ocean floor?
"My sediments (sentiments) exactly."

Did the pilot fly solo?
No, actually he flew pretty high.

Why did the mother bomb scold the baby bomb?
For ticking back.

What city has the most gerbils?
Hamsterdam.

MUDDLED MOTTOES

What's a grease monkey's motto?
Oily to bed, oily to rise.

What's a limousine driver's motto?
The chauffeur (show) must go on.

What's a housemaid's motto?
Look before you sweep.

What's a baker's motto?
Dough or die.

What's a funeral director's motto?
Die now, pay later.

What's a hanging judge's motto?
It's better to give than to reprieve (receive).

6
The Scream Team

Where do monsters learn the cha-cha?
In Dance-ylvania (Transylvania).

What do tourists do in Transylvania?
They go frightseeing.

How can you understand something written in Transylvanian?
Get it Transylated (translated).

How does a one-eyed monster applaud?
It cy-claps (cyclops).

Was the genie in the magic lamp smart?
Yes, he was a geni-us.

What do you say when choosing a magic lamp?
"Genie, meenie, miney, moe . . ."

Where do giant Eskimos live?
In bigloos.

How does the giant in "Jack and the Beanstalk" hitchhike?
With his Fee Fi Fo thumb.

What monster gets its mouth washed out with soap at every full moon?

A swearwolf.

What duck has two fangs hidden inside its bill?

Count Quackula.

What would you get if you crossed Dracula with a finicky eater?

A vampire that takes one bite and leaves the rest.

What do you get when a monster spills grape juice?

A Franken-stain.

Who helped the Bride of Frankenstein go to the ball?

Her scary godmother.

What monster pulls the most practical jokes?

Prankenstein.

When do monsters play practical jokes?

On April Ghoul's Day.

What trick do zombies teach their dogs?

To play dead.

What do zombies fill with food on warm summer days?
Picnic caskets.

What's the Creature from the Black Lagoon's favorite dessert?
Hot sludge sundaes.

How does the Creature from the Black Lagoon score in basketball?
With a slime dunk (slam dunk).

What do zombie actors drive?
Re-hearses.

What theory do giggling zombies prove?
That there is laugh (life) after death.

What does an angel say when he's ready to go to heaven?
"Blessed (blast) off!"

What did Tinkerbell play with as a young fairy?
Tinker toys.

How far is it from one tree to the next in a forest?
Just a hop, skip, and a stump (jump).

What supernatural creature frightens Santa Claus?
The North Pol-tergeist.

WORDS TO THE WILD

What's an angel's motto?
You get what you pray (pay) for.

What's a zombie's motto?
Die now, pay later.

What's an ancient Egyptian grave robber's motto?
Tomb (time) is money.

Who wrote scary stories in rhyme?
Edgar Allan Poet.

What witch writes mysteries?
Hagatha Christie.

How do witches play their records?
In scareo (stereo).

What did the witch get when she stayed at the inn?
Broom and board.

What did the winner of the witches' contest receive?
Cursed (first) prize.

If the winner of a contest gets first prize, what does the loser get?
Worst prize.

What's a ghost's favorite cereal?
Eerio's (Cheerio's).

What do you call two ghost couples?
A fearsome (foursome).

Why don't mummies make good friends?
They're too wrapped up in themselves.

Why don't astronauts make good friends?
They're not down to earth.

What is E.T.'s spaceship when he's not in it?
M.T. (empty).

What would you get if you crossed E.T. with a cheapskate?
An alien who phones home collect.

Why didn't the Loch Ness Monster answer the door?
It was the serpent's (servant's) day off.

What furry little monsters terrorize Russia?
Kremlins (Gremlins).

What does a witch doctor call it when he performs the same magic twice?
Deja voo-doo.

How does the Sandman carry his sand?
In a napsack (knapsack).

What do little Martians learn at camp?
Arts and spacecrafts.

Who does a zombie share its apartment with?
Its tombmate (roommate).

Why don't zombies pay their bills?
They're deadbeats.

What do you read to little zombies to help them sleep?
Deadtime stories.

Was the ghost quiet?
Yes, it didn't say boo.

Who represents the views of ghosts?
Their spooksperson (spokesperson).

What sports do ghosts compete in?
Scarathons (marathons).

7
Pun & Games

Why do owls get invited to so many parties?
Because they're a hoot to have around.

Why are bunnies fun to have at parties?
They hop till they drop.

What's the difference between a generous host and a nasty snob?
One puts people up and the other puts people down.

What's an amoeba's favorite game?
Divide 'n' Seek.

What game do twins love to play?
Siamese Says.

What game do underachievers named Bart like to play?
Simpson Says.

What do you ask a camel at a tea party?
"One hump (lump) or two?"

What's a mechanic's favorite card game?
Engine (gin) rummy.

What animals make the best poker players?
Bluffalo.

What happened to the zombie the day after he stayed up all night partying?
He was dead on his feet.

What do English country gentlemen do on Saturday nights?
Squire dancing.

Do train conductors do the cha-cha?
No, they do the choo-choo.

What do insect ballerinas dance on?
Mosqui-toes.

How do millionaires dance?
Check-to-check.

What kind of music do dwarfs dance to?
Rock 'n' troll.

What kind of music do ancient scribes dance to?
Rock 'n' scroll.

What kind of music do demolition derby winners dance to?
Wreck 'n' roll.

What kind of music do welders dance to?
Heavy metal.

What kind of music do heroes dance to?
Heavy medal.

What kind of music won't balloons dance to?
Pop music.

What kind of music do convicts dance to?
Rock 'n' parole.

GIVE THEM A BREAK

How do garbage collectors
break up with their girlfriends?
They dump them.

How do mountain climbers
break up with their boyfriends?
They cut ties.

How do parachutists
break up with their boyfriends?
They drop them.

How do amoebas
break up with their girlfriends?
They split.

How do ghosts
break up with their boyfriends?
They disappear.

How do dogs
break up with their girlfriends?
They stop going out.

How do sailors
break up with their girlfriends?
They drift apart.

What large stones are used to make costume jewelry?
Rhino-stones (rhinestones).

Who is the most musical deer?
Do-re-mi-fa-so-la-ti-doe.

Who is the stupidest singer?
Do-re-mi-fa-so-la-ti-dodo.

What do you get when you tear a songbook?
Rip (rap) music.

What is a druggist's favorite song?
"Old MacDonald Had a Pharm-acy."

MOTTO MANIA

What's pantyhose's motto?
Born to run.

What's a hairline's motto?
It's better to give than to recede.

What's Miss Clairol's motto?
Do or dye.

What do lumberjacks say on Halloween?
"Trick or tree!"

What does a diesel engine say on Halloween?
"Truck or treat!"

What does Captain Kirk say on Halloween?
"Trek or treat!"

What amusement park ride is only 12 inches long?
A ruler coaster.

What is Dustin Hoffman's favorite candy?
  Tootsie Rolls.

What is a Jedi Master's favorite toy?
  A yo-yoda.

What's Elvis Presley's favorite amusement park ride?
  A rock 'n' roller coaster.

What ride makes mothers and babies scream?
  A stroller coaster.

8

Classroom Crack-ups

Why did the little stegosaurus stay home from school?
It had a dino-sore (dinosaur) throat.

What do baby architects play with?
City blocks.

What do sailors learn in school?
Their A, B, seas.

What do farmers learn in school?
Their A, B, seeds.

What's a farmer's favorite learning game?
Show 'n' Till.

What's the difference between the way students did their homework years ago and the way they do it today?
Years ago, students worked on a desk, today they work on a disk.

Do straight-A students get engaged?
No, they just go study (steady).

Who trains court jesters?
Fool (school) teachers.

What's harder than cutting school?
Gluing it back together.

What do young bankers learn in school?
How to tell dime (time).

What do you send to get a message to a geometry teacher?
A parallelogram.

What grades did the wasp get in school?
It had a bee average.

What did the bee major in in college?
Buzziness (business).

What kind of colleges do plants attend?
Ivy league.

How do students know the cost of education will go up?
In-tuition.

How do musicians prepare for exams?
By studying their notes.

What do musicians mix chemicals in?
Test tubas (tubes).

What English course
do mummies take in school?
De-composition.

What's an English composition teacher's motto?
Essay come, essay go.

What do you call it when you write complete compositions on walls, indenting sentences that contain separate ideas?
Para-graffiti.

What would you get if you crossed the Big Dipper with a zebra?
Stars and stripes.

What scientists dig through layers of dirt to find pieces of Noah's boat?
Arkeologists (archaeologists).

Was Ben Franklin surprised when he discovered electricity?
Oh yes, he was shocked.

9
Show Far–
Show Good

How is an actor like a football player?
They both perform plays.

How do actors live life?
One play (day) at a time.

How is a klutz like an actor?
*When a klutz takes a flop, he can end up in a cast—
when an actor is in a cast, he can end up in a flop.*

What did the director say to the actor with a bad back?
    "Lights, camera, traction!"

What did the bald actor ask himself?
    "Toupee (to be) or not toupee, that is the question."

What do superstitious Jedis carry?
    Good Luke charms.

What singer hosts a talk show?
    Madonnahue.

What pretty fruit hosts a game show?
    Banana White.

What's a hurricane's favorite game show?
"Wind, Lose or Draw."

What's a gunslinger's favorite game show?
"Let's Make a Duel."

Why did Walt Disney go to the mechanic?
For a car-toon up (tune-up).

What's the most frightening cartoon series?
"The Scare (Care) Bears."

What cartoon character is always throwing up?
Barf Simpson.

Who is the most impolite cartoon character?
The Ruderunner.

What do you call a repeat of a Roadrunner cartoon?
A rerun-ner.

What cartoon must be handled with care?
Fragile (Fraggle) Rock.

How do circus dogs fly through the air?
With the greatest of fleas.

What did the seven dwarfs sing when they worked for Santa Claus?
"Hi ho-ho-ho, hi ho-ho-ho, it's off to work we go . . ."

What do animal trainers have when they're too nervous to work?

Cage fright.

What do Moe, Larry and Curly have when they're too nervous to work?

Stooge fright.

What band can't play music?
A rubber band.

What do soldiers play on the radio?

Pla-tunes (platoons).

What would you get if you crossed a portable radio with a stick of dynamite?

A BOOM box.

Who is the chubbiest singer?

Do-re-mi-fatso (do-re-mi-fa-so).

What would you get if you crossed Miss Piggy with a conceited singer?

A little piggy that sings "me me me" all the way home.

What would you get if you crossed a comedian with a boxer?

A comic who knocks you out with his punch line.

How do comedians measure their speed?

In smiles per hour.

What comic team was late for every performance?

Laurel and Tardy (Hardy).

What comic trio lives in the North Pole?

Larry, Curly, and Eski-mo (Moe).

What comic trio has a Native American in it?

Larry, Curly, and Geronimo.

Where do comedians go when they retire?

To an old jokes (folks) home.

What do fish like to listen to for entertainment?

Sand-up comedy.

What do magicians say to make swarms of hungry insects disappear?

"Locust pocus."

What is the phone company's favorite musical?

"Phantom of the Opera-tor."

What's the difference between a relaxed surfer and a beauty queen in a parade?

One floats on top of a wave, the other waves on top of a float.

What's the difference between constellations and Hollywood?

Nothing—in both the stars make pictures.

What's a mechanic's favorite movie?

"Chassis (Lassie) Come Home."

What is the most boring Clark Gable film?

"Yawn With the Wind."

What Disney movie stars people, cartoon characters and C3PO?

"Who Framed Roger Robot?"

What's the difference between Peter Pan and someone who quit the bomb squad?

> *One doesn't want to be grown up, and the other doesn't want to be blown up.*

Who did Charlie the Tuna take to the movies?

> *His gillfriend.*

Who did the tornado take to the movies?

> *Its whirlfriend.*

What movies do two-headed monsters star in?

> *Double creature features.*

What movies make people cry?
  E-motion pictures.

What Star Trek character has a crooked smile?
  Captain Smirk.

What dog went to Oz to take pictures?
  Pho-toto.

If Dorothy hadn't found the Tinman in time, what would his tombstone have said?
  "Rust in Peace."

What did the cowboy say as Mr. Potato Head rode off into the sunset?
  "Who was that mashed man?"

10

Jock Around The Clock

Where do millionaires work out?
> *At wealth clubs.*

What's a bee's favorite sport?
> *Sting-pong.*

What kind of bike riding do dogs do?
> *Fleastyle (freestyle).*

What kind of attitude does a patient fisherman need?
> *Bait (wait) 'n see.*

What's the difference between a baseball player and a Boy Scout?

> *One plays during innings, the other plays during outings.*

What's the difference between a baseball player and a card shark?

> *One steals bases, the other steals aces.*

Why do baseball players make good friends?
> *They always go to bat for you.*

How did the warlock explain his team's nohitter?
> *Pitchcraft.*

Why can't pitchers make decisions?
> *They're always changing their mounds (minds).*

Did you ever ask yourself this silly question:
How come when fighters box, it's timed in rounds?
> *Shouldn't it be timed in squares?*

What does a sweatshirt become when you wear it in the rain?

A wet shirt.

What's a truck driver's favorite sport?

Clutch (touch) football.

Where do high jumpers store their valuables?

In a pole vault.

What do mountaineers do when they're bored?

Climb the walls.

KOOKY CONTESTS

What sport do bananas compete in?
Track and peeled.

What sport do losers compete in?
Track and failed.

What sport do pancakes compete in?
Stack and field.

What sport do dimwits compete in?
Track and Fooled.

What would you get if you crossed C3PO with a gymnast?
An ac-robot.

What do fighters wear under their uniforms?
Boxer shorts.

What did the dugout sampler say?
"Home-run sweet home-run."

Why can't you get a straight answer from wrestlers?
>*They're hard to pin down.*

What kind of foot do you get when you hit it with a golf club?
>*A swollen-one (hole-in-one).*

What do you get if you hit a gopher with a golf club?
>*A mole-in-one.*

What would you get if you crossed an optimist with a boxer?
>*A fighter who's upbeat even when he's beat up.*

What can run even when you're walking?
> *Pantyhose.*

Where does a DJ play sounds of horseback riding and cattle roping?
> *On a rodeo (radio) station.*

What kind of skirts do basketball players wear?
> *Hoop skirts.*

How far is it from one basketball court to the next?
> *Just a hoop, skip and a jump.*

How do you cheer a basketball player?
> *"Hoop Hoop Hooray!"*

11
Win Some, Lose Some

What did Noah say just before the race?
  "On your ark, get set, go."

Why don't sticks of dynamite like to race?
  They always come in blast (last) place.

Why did the match burn the man?
  Because the man struck it first.

What was the heroic daisy awarded?
  A petal of honor.

Why did the quartz rock start an argument?
> *It was tired of being taken for granite (granted).*

What would you get if you crossed a middle class person with an upper class person?
> *A snob who takes the bus, but only after he buys the bus company.*

What would you get if you crossed a gunfighter with a coward?
> *A cowboy who won't show up for a showdown.*

What title did Bullwinkle's beautiful sister win?
> *Moose Universe.*

SAY IT AGAIN, SAM

What's a fish's motto?
Where there's a gill, there's a way.

What's a tailor's motto?
Two threads are better than one.

What's a turtle's motto?
All's shell that ends shell.

What does a hired hand become when he makes too many mistakes?
A fired hand.

What would you get if you crossed a pauper with a millionaire?
A person who can't afford a wallet big enough to put all of his money in.

What would you get if you crossed Mary Sunshine with Gloomy Gus?

> *An optimist who always hopes things will get better, but knows that they won't.*

What illness makes you forget to blow your nose?

> *Amsneezia (amnesia).*

What't the difference between Conan the Barbarian and Henny Penny?

> *One is a warrior, the other is a worrier.*

What chicken wrote fairytales with her chick?

> *Hens Christian And-her-son (Hans Christian Andersen).*

Who are the two stupidest nursery rhyme characters?
> *Tweedle Dee and Tweedle Dumb-Dumb.*

Who is the most boring nursery rhyme character?
> *Blah Blah (Baa Baa) Black Sheep.*

Who is a ghost's favorite nursery rhyme character?
> *Little Boy Boo.*

What do tornadoes fight in?
> *Whirl Wars.*

When do hurricanes stop?
> *Mon-sooner or later.*

What's a raindrop's motto?
> *Two's company, three's a cloud.*

What does Darth Vader take to get from the basement to the roof of his high-rise?
> *The ele-Vader.*

What Space Shuttle pilots always bungle their missions?
> *Disastronauts.*

How do you describe a poor carpet salesman who became a millionaire?
> *He went from rugs (rags) to riches.*

What gamblers went up a hill to fetch a pail of water?
Jackpot and Jill.

What did the horse say when it lost the race?
"Whoa (woe) is me!"

Isn't that a beautiful French tower?
Yes, it's an eyeful (Eiffel).

What do dogs buy from travel agencies?
Hound trip (round trip) tickets.

What did the dog say when it was tenth in a 10-dog race?
"Last, but not leashed!"

12
Show Stoppers

What monster hangs around talk shows?
The Phantom of the Oprah.

Where do talk show hosts go for sun and fun?
To the Geraldo Riviera.

What does a maple tree like to watch on TV?
Sap operas.

What do disc jockeys surf on?
Radio waves.

FUN AND GAME SHOWS

What's a wild cat's favorite TV show?
"Leopardy."

What's a gunfighter's favorite TV show?
"Win, Lose or Draw."

What's a dolphin's favorite TV show?
"Whale of Fortune."

What do horses do for entertainment?
Watch Stable TV.

How is a smashed TV set like a retired surgeon?
Neither one operates anymore.

What's Danny Devito's favorite cookie?
Shortbread.

What famous puppet ate curds and whey?
Little Miss Muppet.

What singing chipmunk designs jeans?
Alvin Klein.

What spaghetti sings opera?
Pasta primadonna.

What brand of fruit punch do sopranos drink?
Hi C.

What is grey, wrinkled and sings songs?
Babar Streisand.

Who gives you a haircut, a shave and a song?
Barber Streisand.

CARTOON COMICS

What cartoon character lives in Jellystone Park
and eats health food?
Yogurt Bear.

What does Boo Boo Bear drink?
Yogi Beer.

What do you call a cartoon about
Humphrey Bogart in Jellystone Park?
Bogi Bear.

What do you say when you want a horse to sing an encore?
"Mare! Mare!"

What does Fred Flintstone sing while he drives?
Car tunes.

What did Humphrey Bogart say to the fish at the piano?
"Play it again, Salmon."

What is a cowboy's favorite movie?
"Lasso Come Home."

Who is the tallest Jedi?
Luke Skyscraper.

In which Star Wars movie did Darth Vader play a referee?
"The Umpire Strikes Back."

What did the glamorous ape wear to the Hollywood opening?
A monk stole.

Why was the actor's hair always messy?
Because he never had a good part.

What is a musician's favorite cereal?
  Flute Loops.

What musical instrument does a crabby Scot play?
  The nagpipes.

What's a weatherman's favorite musical instrument?
  A foghorn.

Why won't weathermen tell each other jokes?
  They don't want to laugh up a storm.

What chord is the hardest to play on a guitar?
  A telephone cord.

MUSICAL CHEERS

What's a bee's favorite musical?
"Stinging in the Rain."

What is a millionaire's favorite musical?
"Guys and Doll-ars."

What is a fish's favorite musical?
"Coral Line."

What is a dog's favorite musical?
"The Hound (Sound) of Music."

What deodorant does a popular musician use?
Rock and roll-on.

Why did the soda bottle take music lessons?
It wanted to be a band liter.

What did the band leader say to the barber?
"Take it from the top."

Why did the outfielder join the orchestra?
So he could play first bass.

What do you call a ballerina when she's late?
Leotard-y.

What did the ballerina buy at the hardware store?
A tutu-by-four.

What does a ballerina have drawn on her arm?
A ta-tutu.

How do native American ballerinas dance?
On their teepee toes.

Where do bad jokes serve time?
In the pun-itentiary.

How do comics like their eggs cooked?
Funny-side-up.

What is a hockey player's favorite brand of comedy?
Slapstick.

Why did the whale leave show business?
It wanted to get out of the spoutlight.

13
Haunted Howls

Why did Casper the Friendly Ghost always ride up in the elevator?

He wanted to lift his spirits.

Who turns into a tired animal at every full moon?

A wearywolf (werewolf).

What is invisible, weighs 2,000 pounds and eats peanuts?

An ele-phantom.

Why do so many monsters become great photographers?
Because they love being in dark rooms.

What did Frankenstein climb to get to his room?
Mon-stairs.

What is the first thing Frankenstein reads in the daily paper?
The horror-scopes.

Who does Frankenstein take to the movies?
His ghoulfriend.

What do you call it when a warlock thinks about his girl-friend?
Witchful (wishful) thinking.

What do witch doctors say when they get married?
"*I voodoo.*"

What do wizards serve tea in?
Cups and sorcerers.

What do you get when King Kong slips on a glacier?
Crushed ice.

What happens when King Kong steps on a piano?
It goes flat.

What did King Kong wear to church?
His Sunday beast (best).

Where does a ghost look up words?
  In a diction-eerie.

How is a regular dictionary different from a witch dictionary?
  In one you learn how to spell words.
  In the other you learn how to word spells.

What did the mixed up witch eat for breakfast?
  Scrambled hex.

What do witches' Rice Krispies say?
  "Snap, cackle, pop!"

What does Big Foot ride to school?
  A bicycle-built-for-toes.

WITCH IS THE FAVORITE?

What's a witch's favorite game?
Hide-and-shriek.

What's a witch's favorite dance?
The hocus-polka.

What's a witch's favorite bird?
The sea ghoul.

What's a witch's favorite Beatles song?
"The Ghoul on a Hill."

What's a witch's favorite song?
"What Kind of Ghoul Am I?"

Where do witches sail?
Off the Pacific ghost.

What do witches put on their front doors?
   Warlocks.

What do warlocks sell at art fairs?
   Witchcrafts.

What do you hear when a witch breaks the sound barrier?
   A sonic broom (boom).

What's the largest spell?
   A jumbo mumbo.

What does Count Dracula drink to stay awake at night?
   Cups of coffin.

Why was Igor the Hunchback so embarrassed?
   Because he made a ghoul of himself.

How did Igor know which horse would win the race?
   He didn't—he just had a hunch.

What did the genie say at the laundromat?
   "I'll grant you three washes."

What do you say when you are attacked by mythical dwarf-like creatures?
   "Sticks and stones may break my bones, but gnomes will never hurt me."

14
Animal Crack-ups

Where did Dumbo the Flying Elephant land?
At the earport.

What does an elephant do when it's frightened?
It ele-faints.

Where do Australians play with their wild animals?
In kanga-rooms.

Where do kangaroos look up words?
In pocket dictionaries.

Who would steal from kangaroos?
Pickpockets.

What famous little deer lives in the town of Bedrock?
Bam Bambi.

What does a brontosaurus do when it sleeps?
Dino-snores.

What does a moose do when it's stuck in traffic?
Honk its horns.

BEARLY FUNNY

What kind of letter does a bear send a lion?
Wild ani-mail.

What kind of bears like to bask in the sunshine?
Solar bears.

What do polar bears use for paste?
I-glue.

What does a Japanese polar bear wear?
An Eskimo-no.

What does a bear use to part her hair?
A honeycomb.

What do you throw at jungle animals when they get married?
Wild rice.

WHAT DO CATS PURR-FUR?

What's a cat's favorite side dish at lunch?
Mice-aroni.

What's a cat's favorite side dish at dinner?
Mice pilaf.

What's a cat's favorite dessert?
Mice cream.

What's a cat's favorite drink?
Miced tea.

What cat eats grass?
A lawn meow-er?

What sound does a turkey judge make?
"Gavel, gavel!"

What do turkeys say when they don't make sense?
"Gobble-dy-gook."

DOGGONE IT!

What is the snootiest dog?
A cocky spaniel.

Where do you look for a missing dog?
At the lost and hound pound.

Where do you buy fresh dog bisquits?
At a barkery.

What do you get when you cross a black dog
and a white dog?
A greyhound.

What do performing dogs do after the show?
Take a bow-wow.

What does a duck say when it's in a rush?
"Quick, quick!"

What does a rooster do with a pencil and paper?
Cock-a-doodles.

Who is the richest animal in the world?
 A mule-ionaire.

When do rabbits fly to Niagara Falls?
 When they're on their bunnymoon.

Who tells us how horses vote?
 A Gallop poll.

What state has the most cows?
 Moo Jersey.

Where can you read up about famous cows?
 In "Moo's Who."

What do giraffes do when they fall in love?
 Neck.

What do sheep wear to keep their hooves warm?
Muttons.

15
Home Silly Home

Where do they keep the Goodyear Blimp?
In a high-rise building.

Where do wealthy painters live?
On easel (easy) street.

What did one entryway think of the other entryway?
That it was a-door-able.

Why did the door get fired?
It was lying down on the knob.

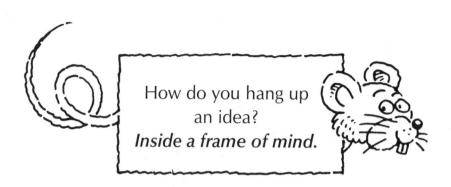

How do you hang up
an idea?
Inside a frame of mind.

Where does a seal hang pictures?
On the living room walrus.

Where can you find the finest basements?
On the best-cellar list.

How can you tell if your porch is bored?
See if it's awning (yawning).

What does a window do when it's cold?
Shutters (shudders).

Where did the table donate money?
To a chair-ity.

How does a chair put on pants?
One leg at a time.

How did the American Indian unlock his door?
With a Chero-key.

How does an American Indian cover the hole in his pants?
With an A-patch-e (Apache).

What do lizards put on their bathroom walls?
Rep-tiles.

What illness did the chimney get?
The flue (flu).

What piece of furniture will never learn to swim?
The sink.

What stove stands alone and wears a mask?
The Lone Range.

What do you take when you have a phone in the bathroom?
Babble baths.

Where do Siamese twins sleep?
  In double beds.

What did the couch say when asked how it was feeling?
  "Sofa (so far), so good."

What do bricklayers clutter their homes with?
  Brick-a-brac.

What happens when knicknacks get scratched?
  They become nicked-nacks.

What was the name of the mixed-up electric company?
  Con Fused.

What does a sheep put over a light bulb?
  A lamb shade.

16
Crazy Eats

Who delivers breakfast, lunch and dinner, and always completes his appointed rounds?
The mealman.

What do Californians eat for breakfast during a tremor?
Earth-Quaker Oats.

What cereal goes, "Snap, crackle, squeak?"
Mice Krispies.

What do you get when you cross a pig and a wildcat?
Sausage lynx.

What does a wacky chef use to get the wrinkles out of pancakes?

A waffle iron.

What does Smokey the Bear spread on his toast?

Forest preserves.

What do millionaires put butter on?

Bankrolls.

What cheese can't stop talking?

Chatter (cheddar) cheese.

What do millionaire first-graders eat for lunch?

Peanut butter and jewelry sandwiches.

What does a slice of toast wear to bed?

Jam-mies.

Where do swimmers sit to eat lunch?

At pool tables.

What is Sigmund Freud's favorite
after-school snack?
  Milk and kookies.

What computer comes with lettuce, tomatoes and special
sauce?
  A Big MacIntosh.

What do you get when you mix Snoopy and Sunday
brunch?
  A beagle and cream cheese.

What do chess players eat for breakfast?
  Pawncakes.

How do scarecrows drink milk shakes?
  Through straws.

What do worms chew?
Wiggley Spearmint Gum.

Who holds the title for the noisiest chewing?
The world chomp-ion.

What do X's and O's put butter on?
Tick-tack-toast.

What is the noisiest food in Italy?
Spaghetti and meatbells.

What brand of spaghetti sauce does a baby eat?
Ragoo goo.

What is a baby's favorite
Chinese dish?
Goo goo gai pan.

What is a bullfighter's
favorite pasta?
   Ravi-olé!

What do silly chefs cook?
   Beef, stew-pid (stupid).

What does the Lone Ranger serve with meatloaf?
   Masked potatoes.

What do foot doctors eat with their hamburgers?
   Bunion rings.

What does Clark Kent turn into when he's hungry?
   Supperman.

What happens to pasta when it laughs too much?
   It gets spa-giddy.

What is a knight's favorite dessert?
   Pie à la moat.

How do you eat evergreen ice cream?
   From pine cones.

What ice cream treat jumped off the Empire State Building?
A banana splat.

How does a gingerbread man close his raincoat?
With gingersnaps.

How does the Pillsbury Doughboy file his cookbooks?
According to the Doughy Decimal System.

What does the Pillsbury Doughboy drink when he's thirsty?
Baking soda.

What does a mean kid get when he eats too much?
A bullyache.

Did the wacky chef kiss the food goodbye?
No, but he micro-waved.

Why was the wacky chef laughing?
Because he cracked a good yolk.

17
Good Sports

What athlete can do everything?
A jock-of-all-trades.

What does a brontosaurus get when he works out too much?
Dino-sore.

Where do small town body-builders hang out?
In hunky-tonks.

What are a prizefighter's favorite colors?
  Black and blue.

Who is the world's most patient person?
  The heavywait champion.

Who is the most popular person at a fist fight?
  The belle of the brawl.

Who is the most violent umpire?
  A rougheree.

What do catcher's eat off of?
  Home plate.

What did Babe Ruth do when
his car wouldn't start?
  He walked home.

When do pigs score in baseball?
  *When the last little piggy runs wee-wee-wee all the
  way home.*

What president can hit a home run and split logs?
  Babe Lincoln.

When train engineers and farmers get together, what sport
do they take part in?
  Track and field.

JOCK JOKES

What is a con man's favorite sport?
Racket ball.

What is a carpet's favorite sport?
Rug-by.

What is a plumber's favorite sport?
Toilet bowl-ing.

How do you win money bowling?
You strike it rich.

When do jockeys control the weather?
When they hold onto the rains.

Why did the golfer need a new club?
Because he had a hole in one.

What do you get when you hit a quarter into a toll booth with your golf club?
> *A toll-in-one.*

What do you get when you cross a card game with a golf game?
> *An ace in the hole.*

What does Arnold Palmer drink on a cold day?
> *Iced tee.*

How do sheep cheer for their football team?
> *"Sis! Boom! Baa! Baa!"*

Why didn't the football player finish school?
> *Because he was left-back.*

When do football players tell jokes?
> *At laugh time (half time).*

What is Gladys Knight's favorite cheer?
> *"Pip! Pip! Hurray!"*

18
Shop To It!

What do you call the celebration of 200 years of shopping?
> *The buy-centennial.*

How would you describe a boring, ordinary shopping center?
> *Run-of-the-mall.*

What is the heaviest kind of chain?
> *A chain of stores.*

Where do you buy laundry detergent?
> *In a soapermarket.*

Where do you buy knee-highs?
In the sock (stock) market.

Where do flowers shop?
At Blooming-dales.

Where does a store keep its extra clothes?
In a wearhouse (warehouse).

What clothes have too much starch?
Hardwear.

What is a clothing salesperson's favorite game?
Tag of war.

CONSUMER HUMOR

What kind of telephones do imposters buy?
Phoneys.

What kind of parasols do dummies buy?
Dumbrellas.

What kind of timepieces do liars buy?
False alarm clocks.

What kind of stockings do firefighters buy?
Pantyhoses.

Where are good products manufactured?
At a satis-factory.

What lemon buys things at auctions?
The highest bitter.

What mall sells only knives?
A chopping center.

In what shopping center do you meet famous people?
    The Mall of Fame.

How did the Wright brothers find out about the clearance sale?
    They got a flyer.

What happens to business when pants sales are slow?
    It slacks off.

When are dress shops impossible to get into?
    When they're clothesed.

What kind of stores do sailors shop in?
    Boat-iques.

What kind of stores do ghosts shop in?
    Boo-tiques.

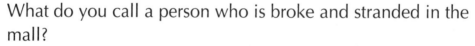

What is the strangest kind of commercial?
    An oddvertisement.

What do you call a person who is broke and stranded in the mall?
    Shopwrecked.

19
Mad Months & Jolidays

When does Santa Claus finish delivering his presents?
Just in the St. Nick of time!

Why are calendars so popular?
Because they have a date every day of the year.

What is a jelly jar's favorite month?
Jam-uary.

What's a liar's favorite month?
Fib-ruary.

BOOBY TRIPS

Where do loser cowboys go on vacation?
To a dud ranch.

Where do bears go on vacation?
To a hiber-nation.

Where does bacteria go on vacation?
Germany.

Where do dieters go on vacation?
Hungary.

When do soldiers get the most tired?
During the month of March.

When do monkeys fall from the sky?
During Ape-ril showers.

How many peanuts do elephants take on vacation?
As many as they can fit in their trunks.

What do you call a chubby jack-o'-lantern?
A plumpkin.

What do magicians say on Halloween?
"Trick—or trick?"

When do you stuff a rubber turkey?
On Pranksgiving.

When do turkeys stop eating?
When they're stuffed.

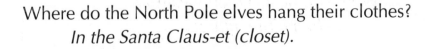

Where do the North Pole elves hang their clothes?
In the Santa Claus-et (closet).

Who sings "Love Me Tender" and makes Christmas toys?
Santa's little Elvis.

What does Santa have for breakfast?
Mistletoast.

When does Mrs. Claus mend Santa's socks?
When they have "ho ho holes."

What insect doesn't like Christmas?
A bah-humbug.

In what movie does Santa meet extraterrestrials?
"Claus Encounters."

Why doesn't peanut butter like Christmas?
Because "T'is the season to be jelly . . ."

What is Scrooge's favorite sandwich?
Grueled cheese.

What do you get when your stockings fall off the fireplace, the ornaments drop off the tree, and Santa tracks soot into your living room?
A merry Christmess.

What is Adam's favorite holiday?
New Year's Eve.

What do you get when you eat too much during the holidays?
A Hippy New Year.

20
Water Water Everywhere

What do you get when you cross a body of water and an important nun?

Lake Superior.

Where does water go when it gets ill?

To the sick bay.

How do you know when a stream needs oil?

It creeks.

Why did the river go on a diet?

To take off a few ponds.

Where do king crabs live?
In sand castles.

What's the most exact body of water?
The Specific Ocean.

What do you get when you cross the United States and the United Kingdom?
The Atlantic Ocean.

What did the Atlantic Ocean say to the Pacific Ocean?
Nothing, it just waved.

Where does seaweed look for a job?
In the Kelp Wanted ads.

What does an ape get when it sits on the beach?
An orangu-tan.

What city has the most beaches?
Sand Francisco.

What do beaches bet on?
Shore (sure) things.

Why couldn't the crab learn to share?
Because it was shellfish.

What kind of lizard loves riddles?
A sillymander.

What do frogs make notes on?
Lily pads.

Why couldn't the mermaid go to college?
Because she was a sea ("C") student.

What boats go to college for free?
Scholar ships.

How do alligators make phone calls?
They croco-dial.

What is the world's slowest ship?
>A snailboat.

What do you call an inexperienced rowboat?
>Wet behind the oars (ears).

Where did the boat go when it had a cold?
>To the doc.

Why are docks so unforgiving?
>Because they harbor grudges.

What do you call it when a boat is influenced by other boats at the dock?
>Pier (peer) pressure.

Where does Snow White park her speedboat?
  At the d'wharf.

What sizes do flat-bottomed boats come in?
  Small, medium and barge.

What do sharks eat with their peanut butter?
  Jellyfish.

Why are rowboats such good listeners?
  Because they're all oars (ears).

How do you mail a boat?
  You ship it.

What do ravens sail in?
  Crowboats.

What do dolphins do when they fall in love?
> *They get down on one fin and porpoise (propose).*

How do fish travel up and down in the ocean?
> *They use an eel-evator.*

Where did the octopus enlist?
> *In the Arms Forces.*

Where do you find a down-and-out octopus?
> *On Squid Row.*

What did Jonah say, when asked how he was feeling?
> *"Very whale, thank you."*

What do whales do when they feel sad?
> *Blubber.*

Where did the fish deposit its allowance?
> *In the river bank.*

21
Bored of Education

Where did your mother's mother learn the ABC's?
> *In gramma school.*

What do farmers learn in school?
> *How to tell ripe from wrong.*

Where do whistles go to school?
> *At insti-toots.*

Why do thermometers go to school?
> *To earn their degrees.*

ODD AND SUBTRACT

What do you get when you add
1 homework assignment and 1 homework assignment?
2 much homework.

What did the spunky yardstick say to its mother?
"I want to stand on my own three feet."

What practical jokes do mathematicians play?
Arithmetricks.

What do mathematicians use to panel
their family rooms?
Multiplywood.

What should you do to help mathematicians
with their back problems?
Put them in sub-traction.

What kind of notebook grows on trees?
Loose leaf.

Why did the student have to take a class in singing?
  Because it was re-choir-ed (required).

How do you know if all the letters of the alphabet are home?
  Peek through the K-hole.

What happens when pants cut school?
  They get suspendered.

Where did cavemen look up synonyms?
  In "Roget's Dinosaurus."

MATH MYTHS

Who do geometry teachers hang around with?
A small circle of friends.

Why couldn't the geometry teacher walk?
He had a sprained angle.

What kind of math do trees learn?
Twigonometry.

Why don't rabbits carry calculators?
Because they multiply so quickly without them.

Why did the computer have to go to the hospital?
It had a terminal illness.

What fruit studies for exams in a hurry?
Cram-berries.

What did the English teacher say to the class clown?
"Comma down!"

HYSTERICAL HISTORY

How did brave Egyptians write?
In hero-glyphics (hieroglyphics).

Who changed King Tut's diapers?
His mummy.

What did medieval kings ride around their castles in?
Moat-er boats.

What did Sir Lancelot wear to bed?
A knightgown.

What ruler was shorter than Napoleon Bonaparte?
A twelve-inch ruler.

What did King George think of the colonies?
That they were revolting.

Where did Abraham Lincoln keep his pigs?
In a hog cabin.

22
Funidentified Flying Objects

How did the radar operator describe the mysterious short-order cook from outer space?
As an unidentified frying object.

What is the messiest constellation?
The Big Diaper.

What keeps the sky from falling down?
Moonbeams.

What is the world's silliest satellite?
  A fool (full) moon.

What is the world's craziest satellite?
  A moonatic.

What planet is shaped like a fish?
  Nep-tuna.

What did the Martian say to the cat?
  "Take me to your litter."

How does E.T. read in bed?
  He turns on a satellight.

What sports do extraterrestrials play?
  Rocket ball.

Why do you need a wrench in the Space Shuttle?
> *To tighten the astronuts.*

What kind of book tells about little green men that don't get along?
> *Science friction.*

What does a vampire wear to a space shuttle launch?
> *A Canaveral Cape.*

Where do extraterrestrials leave their ships?
> *At parking meteors.*

Where do extraterrestrial dentists live?
> *In the molar system.*

What poetry do extraterrestrials write?
> *Uni-verse.*

What do extraterrestrial lambs travel in?
> *Spacesheep.*

Where did the astronaut put his peanut butter sandwich?
> *In his launch box.*

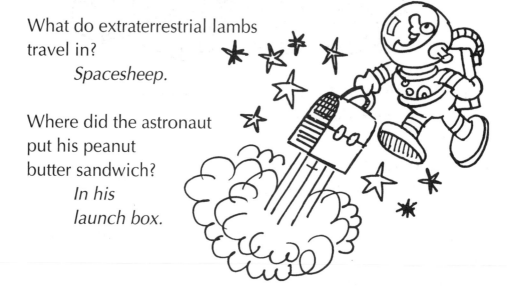

23
Outrageous Outdoors

What did one tornado say to the other tornado?
"Let's blow this town."

When does rainfall make mistakes?
During a blunderstorm.

What do you call it when you holler to someone two miles away?
Lung distance.

What do rich people breathe?
Million-air.

Why wouldn't the lightning bolt go to the storm?
Because it was on strike.

What swept that repulsive hat off your head?
Dis-gust of wind.

Where do crazy plants grow?
In crackpots.

What do you call blue-colored grass?
Smurf turf.

What do you call a national park that everyone gets lost in?
A bewilderness.

When does Kermit the Frog wake up?
At the croak of dawn.

What's the longest rock in the world?
A milestone.

Why was the pile of junk sitting in the middle of the Sahara desert?
For the mirage (garage) sale.

What is the most modest insect?
The humblebee.

What American grasshopper likes to brave the frontier?
Davy Cricket.

What does a cricket use for shaving?
A blade of grass.

What insects stick around bulletin boards?
Thumb ticks.

What kind of stroller do you wheel an infant insect in?
A baby buggy.

Why was the 2,000-year-old flower wrapped in strips of cloth?

It was a chrysanthemummy.

What did the flower say when it was told to keep a secret?
"Mum's the word!"

What did the tree say when it couldn't solve the riddle?
"I'm stumped."

What young tree always gets taken advantage of?
A sap-ling.

What do you get when you chop down a tuna tree?
Fish sticks.

What happened to her little ones when they disobeyed Mother Earth?
They were grounded.

24
Crime & Pun-ishment

What comic strip superhero drinks apple juice and scales tall buildings?

Ciderman.

Where do you send old detectives?

To the clue factory.

What do you call a low-flying police officer?

A helicopper.

Who is the smallest person on the police force?
The centi-meter maid.

Where do police officers put criminals that steal Hershey's chocolate?
Behind candy bars.

What did one police officer say to the other police officer after the bank was robbed?
"It was all your vault."

How do police officers patrol the ocean?
In squid cars.

What did the police officer say to the tired criminal?
"It looks like you could use a-rrest."

Why did the policeman arrest the letter?
He caught the J walking.

Why did government agents arrest the accountant who wouldn't take a cab?
They got him for taxi evasion.

What did they do to the coffee cup after it was arrested?
Took a mug shot.

What did the prisoner say when he bumped into the governor?
"Pardon me!"

What do you do for a prisoner in a leaking boat?
Bail him out.

Why did the clock strike 12?
Because they struck it first.

How did the jewel thief wake up every morning?
To a burglar alarm.

In what state are the most secrets uncovered?
South Decoder.

What kind of hives are most dangerous to scratch?
Bee hives.

What color does purple become when it's angry?
Violet (violent).

Why are saddles so hard to get along with?
Because they stirrup trouble.

What do Butch Cassidy and the Sundance Kid roast over an open fire?
Marshal-mallows.

What young outlaw was overweight?
Belly the Kid.

What do criminals read for fun?
The want-ed ads.

What do you do with a painting of an outlaw?
Hang it at sunrise.

What cowboy steals teapots?
A kettle (cattle) rustler.

What crime-fighting gardener rides a horse and wears a mask?
The Lawn Ranger.

What advice did the attorney give to the American Indian?
Sioux (sue).

What did the attorney say to the milk carton?
"I'll see you in quart."

What did the president of the Lefties Association say?
"We have rights, too."

What do nearsighted lawyers wear?
Contract lenses.

What do hangmen read?
"The Daily Noose."

What do secret agents invest their money in?
James Bonds.

How did Sir Lancelot settle disagreements?
  In knight court.

What did the judge say when the librarian broke the law?
  "I'm going to throw the book at you!"

Who cleans up a judge's office?
  The chamber maid.

What do you call twelve hurt people who judge guilt and innocence?
  An injury.

What happens to words when they break the law?
  They get sentenced.

25
Happily Ever Laughter

Where does Mother Goose leave her garbage?
At the Humpty Dump.

What did the gingerbread man's grandfather use for walking?
A candy cane.

What does Mickey Mouse's girlfriend wear?
Minnie (mini) skirts.

What singing grasshopper lives in a fireplace?
   Chimney Cricket.

What man slept in his clothes for 100 years?
   Rip Van Wrinkled.

What is the name of the story about the athlete and the giant?
   "Jock and the Beanstalk."

What does Jack's giant do when he plays football?
   He fee-fi-fo-fumbles.

What lamb stuck itself with a spindle and fell asleep for 100 years?
   Sheeping Beauty.

What does Sleeping Beauty gargle with?
  Rinse Charming.

What brand of toilet paper does Sleeping Beauty use?
  Prince Charmin.

What happens to stupid princes?
  They get throne (thrown) out.

Where do stupid princes come from?
  Kingdum-dums.

What nursery rhyme chicken
lost her sheep?
  Little Bo Peep-Peep.

What happened to Little Bo Peep
after she spent all day looking for her sheep?
  She was Little Bo Pooped.

What powerful reptile lives in Emerald City?
  The Lizard of Oz.

What heavy snowstorm covered Emerald City?
  The Blizzard of Oz.

What sign did the real estate agent put in front of the Old
Woman Who Lived in a Shoe's house?
  "Soled."

What legendary character steals from the rich and keeps it?
　　Robin Hoodlum.

What dancer spins straw into gold?
　　Rhumba-stiltskin.

What do short fairy tale characters wear to look taller?
　　Rumple-stilts.

Who do mice see when they get sick?
　　The Hickory Dickory Doc.

What did Ali Baba write on?
　　Sandpaper.

Who helped Cinderella's cat go to the ball?
　　Its furry godmother.

26
Drive Yourself Crazy!

What do you call a brainy
locomotive?
A train of thought.

What locomotive wears sneakers?
A shoe-shoe train.

What do you get if you cross a happy puppy with a
locomotive?
Waggin' train.

How can you tell if a train is happy?
It whistles while it works.

What state has the most trains?
Massachoochoo.

How does a train blow bubbles?
With choo-chooing gum.

When time flies, where does the pilot sit?
In the clockpit.

What kind of flying lessons are best to avoid?
Crash courses.

WHEELY FUNNY

What car runs on electricity?
A Voltswagen.

What car can't stop crying?
A Saab (sob).

What's the world's meanest car?
Attila the Hyundai (Hun).

What car can leap tall buildings in a single bound?
A Super-u (Subaru).

What family car doesn't move?
A stationary wagon.

What sea creature is found in every car?
A steering whale.

MECHANIC PANIC

Why did the tailpipe see the mechanic?
It was exhausted.

Why did the car radio see the mechanic?
For a tune-up.

Why did the mechanic call the exterminator?
To get the bugs out of the engine.

Where do mechanics wear earrings?
On their ear lubes (lobes).

What does a car mechanic do when he's 65?
He re-tires.

Why was the silly gasoline pump embarrassed?
Because it made a fuel of itself.

TICKLISH TICKETS

Why did the sheep get a ticket?
For making a ewe (U) turn.

Why did the farmer get a ticket?
He exceeded the seed limit.

Why did the pilot get a ticket?
*For going the wrong way on a runway
(one way) street.*

Why did the swimmer get a ticket?
He was caught diving without a license.

Where do automobiles do the backstroke?
In car pools.

What do you call it when a car hits a candy machine?
A vender bender.

What do cars eat from?
License plates.

Why couldn't the little boy see his bicycle after he parked it
behind a tree?
Because the bark was bigger than his bike.

What is a chauffeur's favorite drink?
> *Limo-nade.*

Where shouldn't you ever park a protein?
> *In front of a carbohydrant.*

Was the blimp crazy?
> *Yes, it was a balloonatic.*

What do you get when a bike freezes?
> *An ice-cycle (icicle).*

What kind of book did Chitty Chitty Bang Bang write about itself?
> *An auto-biography.*

27
Party Lines

What do little potatoes play on in the park?
A tater-totter (teeter-totter).

What did King Kong play on in the park?
The monkey bars.

Where do small camels play?
In sandboxes.

What does a baby snake play with?
A rattle.

What do Japanese children play with?
Tokyo-yos.

What do you call a fun-loving toddler that wears diapers?
A potty (party) animal.

When do candles party?
On wickends.

Where do pickles party?
In a barrel of fun.

What state loves Latino music?
Ala-bamba.

What is the worst flower to invite to a party?
A daffo-dull.

What is the worst musical instrument to play at your party?
A humdrum.

What do you call a musician who pretends he can play the sax?
A saxophone-y.

What music do steel workers play at their parties?
Heavy metal.

How can you find out how many vampires attended the party?

Just count Dracula.

What state has the loudest parties?

Illinoise.

What do monsters use to decorate parties?

Creep (crepe) paper.

COOK OUT BELOW!

Where does a Ken doll grill his hamburgers?
On a Barbie-cue.

Where do monkeys barbecue their hamburgers?
On grillas.

What do cannibals barbecue?
Speared (spare) ribs.

NAME THAT GAME

What is a mouse's favorite game?
Hide 'n squeak.

What is a faucet's favorite game?
Hide 'n leak.

What is a parrot's favorite game?
Hide 'n speak.

What is a thief's favorite game?
Hide 'n sneak.

What is a surfer's favorite game?
Tide 'n seek.

What is a sled's favorite game?
Glide 'n seek.

NAME THAT GAME

What is Dr. Pepper's favorite game?
Follow the Liter.

What is a whale's favorite game?
Swallow the Leader.

What is a fish's favorite game?
Salmon Says.

What is a priest's favorite game?
Ring around the Rosary.

What is a quarterback's favorite game?
Tick-Tackle-Toe.

What is Big Foot's favorite game?
Tick-Tack-Toes.

What is the playground's favorite game?
Slide 'n seek.

What did Fred Astaire and Ginger Rogers put on the floor of their dance studio?
> *Waltz-to-waltz carpeting.*

What do mermaids eat at birthday parties?
> *Fishcakes.*

What is a fish's favorite dance step?
> *The fox-trout (fox trot).*

What did one perfume say to the other perfume?
> *"Cologne at last."*

What do you say when the Lone Ranger wears cologne?
> *"Who was that musked man?"*

Where does a computer go to dance?
> *To a disk-o.*

What do cannibals eat at parties?
> *Lady fingers.*

What musical group performs at marriage ceremonies?
> *A wedding band.*

28
Funny Business

What pen company is in business one day and out of business the next?

Disappearing Inc. (Ink).

When can one man be more than one man?

When he's Foreman.

What do plumbers smoke?

Pipes.

What 20 pound bag of dry food do 30-year old executives buy?

Yuppie Chow.

What vegetables can predict the future?

E. S. Peas.

How do hypnotists get around without a car?

They use public trance-portation.

Where do old ministers go?

Out to pastor (pasture).

Why did the wacky farmer hire a maid?

To dust his crops.

What did the wacky carpenter do before he went to bed each night?

He made his bed.

What do basketmakers do when it's time to go?
Weave goodbye!

Why did the paintbrush retire?
It had a stroke.

How does an artist break up with his girlfriend?
He gives her the brush-off.

What do you call a messy mailman?
A litter carrier.

Why did the dogcatcher catch so many large dogs?
Because he was getting paid by the pound.

Where can you find an unconscious barber?
In a comb-a.

What do you say to a barber when you want him to cut your hair faster?
"Make it snippy!"

Why did the barber win the race?
He knew a short cut.

Where do barbers keep their money?
In shavings banks.

29
Best of the West

Who was the most famous cat in the West?
Kitty Carson.

What western city is named for a ghost?
Casper (Wyoming).

Why do outlaws sleep on the ground after they rob a bank?
Because they want to lie low.

SAY THESE 3 TIMES QUICKLY

Should sheriffs sup at cheap chop suey shops?

The selfish Sheriff should share some shellfish.

The Sheriff shot a shy thrush.

Six sheriffs seek six sick sheiks.

Where is the chief cheap sheep section?

Why did Billy the Kid set Dodge City on fire?
   So he could be the toast of the town.

What was Billy the Kid's favorite subject in school?
   Triggernometry.

Who pulled the biggest holdup in history?
   Atlas—he held up the whole world.

When is it good manners to spit in a rancher's face?
   When his moustache is on fire.

Why was the bowlegged cowboy fired?
   Because he couldn't get his calves together.

What do you call an outlaw armed with four loaded revolvers?
> *"Sir!"*

What kind of fur do you get from outlaws?
> *As fur as you can get.*

Who is the thirstiest cowboy in the West?
> *The one who drank Canada Dry.*

Why was the animal thrown out of the poker game?
> *Because it was a cheetah.*

What kind of cat chases outlaws?
> *A posse cat.*

30
Howdy, Partner

Why did the Sheriff arrest the chicken?
> *It used fowl language.*

What would you get if you crossed Jesse James and Count Dracula?
> *A robbery at the blood bank.*

What kind of pole do you have when five frogs sit on top of each other?
> *A toad-em pole.*

Who is the meanest goat in the West?
   Billy the Kid.

How are goats impolite?
   They're always butting in.

What do you call an undersized goat?
   A peanut butt-er.

What would you have if a young goat fell into a blender?
   A mixed-up kid.

What happened when the goat ate the candle?
   It burped with delight (the light).

If a posse of ten men chased one outlaw, what time would it be?

Ten after one.

How did the Indians get to be the first people in North America?

They had reservations.

What kind of hawk has no wings?

A toma-hawk.

What do you get if you cross a Hawaiian dancer and an Indian brave?

A hula-whoop.

31
Horsin' Around

What did the horse say when it finished a bale of hay?
"Well, that's the last straw!"

When is a horse not a horse?
When it turns into a stable.

How long should a horse's legs be?
Long enough to reach the ground.

Why are horses always poorly dressed?
Because they wear shoes but no socks.

How do you make a horse float?
Take two scoops of ice cream, root beer—and add one horse.

What always follows a horse?
Its tail.

Which part of the horse is most important?
The mane (main) part.

When is a pistol like a young horse?
When it is a Colt.

Why is a rodeo horse rich?
It has a million bucks.

If a millionaire sits on gold, who sits on Silver?
The Lone Ranger.

How much do you have to know to teach a horse tricks?
More than the horse.

Are horses good acrobats?
"Yes, they can turn cartwheels."

Are horses good artists?
"Yes, they can draw carriages."

Where do you send a sick pony?
To the horsepital.

What has four legs and can see just as well from either end?
A horse with its eyes closed.

What kind of horses frighten ranchers?
Nightmares.

32
The Last Roundup

Where do cattle go for entertainment?
To the moovies.

Which newspaper do cattle read?
The Daily Moos.

When was beef at its highest?
When the cow jumped over the moon.

Where do cows dance?
In a dis-cow-teque.

Where do cattle dance?
At the meatball.

What do you call a cow that has lost its calf?
De-calf-inated.

What is a calf after it is a year old?
Two years old.

What key do cattle sing in?
Beef-flat (B-flat).

What is the easiest way to keep milk from turning sour?
Leave it in the cow.

Why did the rancher take the cow to the vet?
Because she was so mooo-dy.

What kind of automobiles do rich steers drive?
Cattle-lacs.

How do cowboys drive steers?
With steer-ing wheels.

What is the quickest way to count cows?
On a cow-culator.

What do you call a sleeping bull?
A bull dozer.

Why did the cow go to the psychiatrist?
Because it had a fodder complex.

What cattle follow you wherever you go?
Your calves.

Why don't cows have money?
Because people milk them dry.

What do cows give after an earthquake?
Milk shakes.

What do you get when a herd of cattle stampedes through a vegetable garden?
Squash.

Where do calves eat?
In calf-eterias.

Where do cattle eat?
In re-steer-rants.

What goes out black and comes in white?
A black cow in a snowstorm.

Why don't most cows go to college?
>*Because not many graduate from high school.*

How is a political speech like a steer?
>*There's a point here and there and a lot of bull in between.*

What would you have if cattle fought each other?
>Steer Wars.

What do you call a cattle rustler?
>*A beef-thief.*

How do you make meatloaf?
>*Send a cow to the seashore.*

What is the most important use for cowhide?
To keep the cow together.

Why is it better to own a cow than a bull?
Because a cow gives milk, but a bull always charges.

What is the best thing to do if a bull charges you?
Pay him.

How do you keep a bull from charging?
Take away his credit cards.

If a cow could talk, what would it say?
Udder nonsense.

What would you get if you crossed a chicken and a cow?
Roost beef.

33
Inlaws & Outlaws

Why were outlaws the strongest men in the Old West?
They could hold up trains.

What kind of outlaw steals soap and towels?
A dirty crook.

Why did the banana run from the outlaw?
Because it was yellow.

What happened to the outlaw who fell into the cement mixer?

> *He became a hardened criminal.*

What did the outlaw get for holding up the rubber band factory?

> *A long stretch.*

What did the outlaw get for stealing the calendar?

> *Twelve months.*

Why did the outlaw try to steal the dictionary?

> *He heard there was "money" in it.*

Why did the outlaw hold up air-conditioned banks?

> *To get cold cash.*

Why did the outlaw gang try to steal the baseball field?
    Because it was the biggest diamond in the world.

What happened when the outlaw ran away with the circus?
    The Sheriff made him bring it back.

What happened when the outlaws and the posse jumped
out of the plane?
    They had a chute out.

What is better than presence of mind when you meet an
outlaw gang?
    Ansence of body.

What is the safest way to talk to an outlaw?
    By long distance.

What happened when the painter threw his pictures at the outlaw?

The outlaw had an art attack.

When is an outlaw neither left-handed nor right-handed?

When he is underhanded.

What is the difference between an outlaw and a church bell?

One steals from the people—the other peals from the steeple.

What did the victim say when the outlaw stuffed a dirty piece of cloth in his mouth?

"That's an old gag."

Why did the outlaw put a pistol in each pocket of his jacket?

> *He wanted a coat of arms.*

Why did the outlaw hold up the river?
> *He heard it had two banks.*

How many outlaws can you put into an empty cell?
> *One. After that the cell isn't empty anymore.*

Why did the outlaw steal the deck of cards?
> *He heard there were 13 diamonds in it.*

Why did the outlaw hold up the bakery?
> *He kneaded the dough.*

Why can't an outlaw living in Texas be buried in Oklahoma?
> *Because he's still living!*

Why was the outlaw buried in the town cemetery?
> *Because he was dead.*

What do you get if an outlaw band falls into the ocean?
> *A crime wave.*

What is more frightening than one mean outlaw?
> *Two mean outlaws.*

Why did the gang of outlaws suddenly leave the restaurant?
> *Because they had finished eating.*

What kind of album is put out by a bunch of outlaws?
A criminal record.

What does a train do when an outlaw chases it?
It makes tracks.

What do you call a short, sunburned outlaw riding a horse?
Little Red Riding Hood.

What kind of bars won't keep an outlaw in jail?
Chocolate bars.

How do you treat an outlaw with an itchy trigger finger?
With respect.

What do you call an outlaw with cotton stuffed in his ears?
Anything you want. He can't hear you.

What kind of outlaws wear suspenders?
Hold-up men.

What do you get if you cross a big bell and an outlaw?
A gongster.

Why did the outlaw take a shower before he broke out of jail?
He wanted to make a clean getaway.

34
Ride 'Em, Cowboy!

What did the tenderfoot see when he fell off his horse?
An all-star show.

Why do cowboys ride horses?
Because the horses are too heavy to carry.

210

What did the cowboy say to the horse he hadn't seen in a long time?

"I forget your name, but your pace is familiar."

What season is it when a tenderfoot tries to ride a stallion?

Fall.

When is a cowboy most like a pony?

When he's a little hoarse.

Why did the cowboy saddle up the phonograph record?

He wanted to be a disc jockey.

Why did the cowboy saddle up a porcupine?

So he wouldn't have to ride it bareback.

What is the hardest thing about learning to ride a bucking horse?

>The ground.

What does a cowboy say to his horse after a 100-mile ride?
>"Whoa!"

What has six legs and walks with only four?
>*A horse and rider.*

Why did the cowboy ignore the
"Danger" sign on the cliff?
   Because he thought it was only a bluff.

What musical note do you hear when a horse falls on a
man who's digging for gold?
   A-flat minor.

What has two arms, two wings, two tails, three heads. three
bodies and eight legs?
   A cowboy on horseback holding a chicken.

35
Smile When You Say That

What is green and has two legs and a trunk?

A stagecoach passenger with motion sickness.

How do cowboys watch TV when they're out on the range?

By communication saddle lights (satellites).

Why did the cowboy put up his tent on the stove?
So he could have a home on the range.

What song do bored cowboys sing?
"Ho-hum on the Range."

Why did the muddy chicken cross the road twice?
Because it was a dirty double crosser.

What happened after the cowboy drank eight Cokes?
He burped 7-Up.

How did the Sheriff find the missing barber?
He combed the town.

What did the termite say
when he came into the
saloon?
*"Is the bar
tender here?"*

What is a sheep's favorite snack?
A bah-loney sandwich.

Why are sheep poor?
Because they're always being fleeced.

What does a sheep say when it has problems?
"Where there's a wool, there's a way."

What would you get if you crossed a porcupine and a sheep?
An animal that could knit its own sweaters.

What do well-behaved lambs say to their mothers?
"Thank ewe."

What does a male sheep do when he gets angry?
He goes on a ram-page.

What did the cowboy say when he wanted to get the sheep's attention?
"Hey, ewe!"

If dogs have fleas, what do sheep have?
Fleece.

Why do sheep go into saloons?
To look for the bah-tender.

Where do cowboys take their sheep for a haircut?
To the bah-bah shop.

What would you have if a masked outlaw were run over by stampeding cattle?

The Mashed Bandit.

What would you have if Batman and Robin were run over by stampeding cattle?

Flatman and Ribbon.

What did the picture say to the Sheriff?

"I've been framed!"

What kind of band seldom makes music?

An outlaw band.

What do buffaloes celebrate every 200 years?
  Their Bison-tennial.

What would happen if an ice cream cone picked a fight with Jesse James?
  The ice cream cone would get licked.

What do you call Jesse James when he has the flu?
  A sick shooter.

Why did Jesse James shoot the clock?
  He wanted to kill time.

SAY THESE 3 TIMES QUICKLY

Sharpshooters should shoot slowly.

Sixty-six sick six-shooters.

"The sharpshooters are shipshape, sir."

A genuine judge just judges justly.

Good gunsmoke—bad gunsmoke.

Six cattle slip on slick ski slopes.

No stagecoach stops at Smith's fresh fishsauce shop.

What goes all around a ranch but doesn't move?
    A fence.

Why did the cowboy put his bunk in the fireplace?
    So he could sleep like a log.

Why did the cowboy run around his bunk?
    So he could catch up on his sleep.

Why did the cowboy take a hammer to bed with him?
    So he could hit the hay.

What is the difference between a sharpshooter and
chocolate cake?
    One hits the mark—the other hits the spot.

Why did the sharpshooter carry a ruler?
    So he could shoot straight.

Index

223